California Science

Science Study Notebook

PEARSON
Scott
Foresman

Editorial Offices: Glenview, Illinois • Parsippany, New Jersey • New York, New York
Sales Offices: Boston, Massachusetts • Duluth, Georgia • Glenview, Illinois • Coppell,
Texas • Sacramento, California • Mesa, Arizona

Series Authors

Dr. Timothy Cooney
*Professor of Earth Science and
Science Education*
University of Northern Iowa (UNI)
Cedar Falls, Iowa

Dr. Jim Cummins
Professor
Department of Curriculum, Teaching,
and Learning
University of Toronto
Toronto, Canada

Dr. James Flood
*Distinguished Professor of Literacy and
Language*
School of Teacher Education
San Diego State University
San Diego, California

Barbara Kay Foots, M.Ed.
Science Education Consultant
Houston, Texas

Dr. M. Jenice Goldston
*Associate Professor of Science
Education*
Department of Elementary Education
Programs
University of Alabama
Tuscaloosa, Alabama

Dr. Shirley Gholston Key
*Associate Professor of Science
Education*
Instruction and Curriculum Leadership
Department
College of Education
University of Memphis
Memphis, Tennessee

Dr. Diane Lapp
*Distinguished Professor of Reading
and Language Arts in Teacher
Education*
San Diego State University
San Diego, California

Sheryl A. Mercier
Classroom Teacher
Dunlap Elementary School
Dunlap, California

Karen L. Ostlund, Ph.D.
UTeach Specialist
College of Natural Sciences
The University of Texas at Austin
Austin, Texas

Dr. Nancy Romance
*Professor of Science Education &
Principal Investigator*
NSF/IERI Science IDEAS Project
Charles E. Schmidt College of Science
Florida Atlantic University
Boca Raton, Florida

Dr. William Tate
*Chair and Professor of Education and
Applied Statistics*
Department of Education
Washington University
St Louis, Missouri

Dr. Kathryn C. Thornton
*Former NASA Astronaut
Professor*
School of Engineering and Applied
Science
University of Virginia
Charlottesville, Virginia

Dr. Leon Ukens
Professor Emeritus
Department of Physics, Astronomy,
and Geosciences
Towson University
Towson, Maryland

Steve Weinberg
Consultant
Connecticut Center for Advanced
Technology
East Hartford, Connecticut

Contributing Author

Dr. Michael P. Klentschy
Superintendent
El Centro Elementary School District
El Centro, California

Consulting Author

Dr. Olga Amaral
Chair, Division of Teacher Education
San Diego State University
Calexico, California

ISBN: 0-328-23647-0

Copyright © Pearson Education, Inc.

All Rights Reserved. Printed in the United States of America.
This publication is protected by Copyright, and permission
should be obtained from the publisher prior to any prohibited
reproduction, storage in a retrieval system, or transmission
in any form by any means, electronic, mechanical,
photocopying, recording, or likewise. For information
regarding permission(s), write to: Permissions Department,
Scott Foresman, 1900 East Lake Avenue, Glenview, Illinois
60025.

4 5 6 7 8 9 10 11 12 V001 15 14 13 12 11 10 09 08 07

© Pearson Education, Inc.

Unit A
Physical Sciences

Unit B
Life Sciences

© Pearson Education, Inc.

Unit C
Earth Sciences

© Pearson Education, Inc.

Using Your Science Study Notebook

The *Science Study Notebook* is your companion as you read and study your science textbook. It will help you take notes as you read and learn vocabulary words. It also will help you record results as you conduct science activities. You can use the following pages for each chapter in your textbook.

- In the **Chapter Study Guide,** preview the main ideas in the chapter by completing an outline as you look at the pages.

- Cut out **Vocabulary Cards** and use them to learn the meaning of the words.

- Use the **Vocabulary Preview** to find words in the glossary to help you match the word with the definition.

- As you do the **Directed Inquiry Activity,** record your results and answer the questions to explain your results.

- Use a graphic organizer to record your answers for the **How to Read Science** page in your textbook.

- As you read each lesson, use the **Lesson Study Guide** to take notes and organize the main ideas. Later you can use your notes to prepare for tests.

- As you do the **Guided Inquiry Activity,** record data in charts and answer questions to explain your results.

- At the end of each unit, you will conduct an experiment in the **Full Inquiry Activity.** Write your hypothesis, record and interpret data, and write your conclusions.

© Pearson Education, Inc.

Science Safety

Scientists know they must work safely when doing experiments.
You need to be careful when doing science activities too.
Follow these safety rules:

- Read the activity carefully before you start.

- Listen to the teacher's instructions. Ask questions about things you do not understand.

- Wear safety goggles when needed.

- Keep your work area neat and clean.

- Clean up spills right away.

- Never taste or smell substances unless directed to do so by your teacher.

- Handle sharp items and other equipment carefully.

- Use chemicals carefully.

- Help keep plants and animals that you use safe.

- Tell your teacher if you see something that looks unsafe or if there is an accident.

- Put materials away when you finish.

- Dispose of chemicals properly.

- Wash your hands well when you are finished.

© Pearson Education, Inc.

Building Blocks of Matter

In this chapter, you will learn about matter. You will learn that all matter is made up of elements, which are made up of atoms. You will learn that elements are organized in the periodic table and can be classified as metals, nonmetals, and metalloids. You will also learn that elements can form compounds. Compounds and elements can form mixtures, whose substances can be separated.

Tell What You Know

What makes up all matter?

_____

Preview the Chapter

Page through each lesson to preview the content and the pictures. Complete the outline by filling in the lesson titles and subheads. Describe your favorite pictures.

Lesson 1: _____

_____

_____

_____

Favorite Picture: _____

Lesson 2: _____

_____

_____

_____

_____

_____

© Pearson Education, Inc.

Name _____

_____

_____

_____

_____

Favorite Picture: _____

Lesson 3: _____

_____

_____

_____

_____

Favorite Picture: _____

Lesson 4: _____

_____

_____

_____

_____

Favorite Picture: _____

Now you have a Chapter Study Guide. As you read each
lesson, you can write notes on your Study Guide.

Notes for Home: Your child previewed Chapter 1, which tells about matter and
its composition. Have your child compare compounds and mixtures.

© Pearson Education, Inc.

✂

element	**physical property**
Chapter 1, Lesson 1	Chapter 1, Lesson 1
chemical property	**atom**
Chapter 1, Lesson 1	Chapter 1, Lesson 2
atomic number	**molecule**
Chapter 1, Lesson 2	Chapter 1, Lesson 2
compound	**solution**
Chapter 1, Lesson 3	Chapter 1, Lesson 4

 Directions: Cut out the boxes to use as vocabulary cards.

© Pearson Education, Inc.

any property of a material that can be seen or measured without changing the material

one of more than 100 basic kinds of matter that cannot be broken into smaller pieces through physical or chemical processes

the smallest particle of an element with the same properties of the element

any property of a material that describes how it changes into other materials

the smallest part of a substance made from more than one atom that still has the properties of that substance

the number of protons in the nucleus of an atom; the single most important property of an element

a mixture in which substances are spread out evenly and will not settle

a kind of matter made of a chemical combination of two or more elements

Directions: Cut out the boxes to use as vocabulary cards.

© Pearson Education, Inc.

Name _____

Chapter 1 Vocabulary

Find each word in your glossary at the back of your book.
Read its meaning. Then write the letter of the meaning on the
line next to the word.

____ **1.** element

____ **2.** physical property

____ **3.** chemical property

____ **4.** atom

____ **5.** atomic number

____ **6.** molecule

____ **7.** compound

____ **8.** solution

a. any property of a material that describes how it changes into other materials

b. the number of protons in the nucleus of an atom

c. one of more than 100 basic kinds of matter that cannot be broken into smaller pieces through physical or chemical processes

d. a mixture in which substances are spread out evenly and will not settle

e. the smallest part of a substance made from more than one atom that still has the properties of that substance

f. the smallest particle of an element that has the same properties of the element

g. a kind of matter made of a chemical combination of two or more elements

h. any property of a material that can be seen or measured without changing the material

Identify each of these as a physical property or a chemical property.

9. weight: _____

10. flammability: _____

Notes for Home: Your child is learning these vocabulary words in Chapter 1.
Name a term and ask your child to describe it.

© Pearson Education, Inc.

Name _____

Explore: How do properties change during a chemical reaction?

Be careful!

Wear safety goggles. Do not taste the tablet or liquid.

Record your observations.

Tablet in cold water Temperature:	
Tablet in warm water Temperature:	

Explain Your Results

1. How did some properties change?

_____

_____

2. **Infer** Draw a conclusion about the way temperature affected the speed of the reaction.

_____

_____

 Notes for Home: Your child did an activity involving a chemical reaction.
Home Activity: Talk with your child about how he or she knew a chemical reaction took place. (The formation of a gas evidenced by bubbles)

Science Study Notebook

© Pearson Education, Inc.

Name _____

Make Inferences

Apply It!

Complete the graphic organizer after reading page 7.

Facts

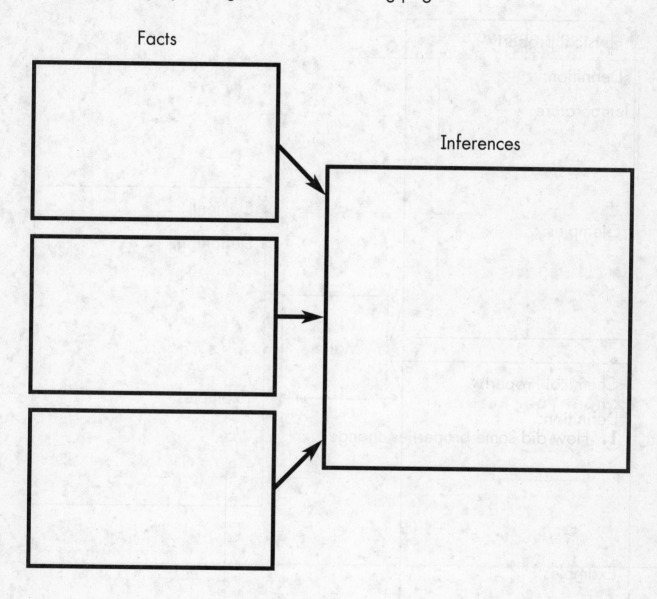

Inferences

© Pearson Education, Inc.

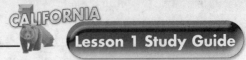

What are properties of matter?

Describe matter by defining the following and give examples of each.

Physical property

Definition:

Examples:

Matter

Element

Definition:

Examples:

Chemical Property

Definition:

Examples:

Notes for Home: Your child defined and gave examples of the physical and chemical properties of matter. Have your child identify physical properties of an item you hold up. Challenge your child to name at least 6 properties.

© Pearson Education, Inc.

Science Study Notebook

Name _____

What makes up matter?

Summarize the information given for each part of the lesson.

Atoms and Elements
Molecules
Images of Molecules
Elements and the Periodic Table
Classifying Elements
Information on the Periodic Table
Groups and Periods
Metals and Their Properties
Metal Mixtures

 Notes for Home: Your child summarized information about elements and the periodic table. Ask your child to explain the organization of the periodic table.

© Pearson Education, Inc.

What are compounds?

Write each of these descriptions in the chart. Place descriptions that apply to any compound in the **Compound** side of the chart. Place descriptions that apply to salts in the **Salt** side of the chart.

It has at least one metal and one nonmetal element.

NaCl is the formula for a common salt.

It can be formed by sharing electrons.

It is formed by the reaction of a base and an acid.

It is a combination of two or more elements.

It dissolves in water.

Sugar is made up of oxygen, hydrogen, and carbon.

It is held together by opposite charges.

H_2O is the formula for water.

It forms crystals.

It melts only at very high temperatures.

Compound	Salt

Notes for Home: Your child identified characteristics of compounds in general and of salts specifically. Have your child demonstrate how salt dissolves in water.

© Pearson Education, Inc.

How can we separate mixtures?

Read each list. Then write a statement to tell what the list describes.

1. take carrots out of a soup
2. use a filter to remove sand from water
3. use a magnet to attract metals

_____

1. Solvent dissolves a substance. Water is a solvent.
2. Solute is the substance dissolved. Sugar is a solute.

_____

1. made of only one kind of atom
2. have a chemical symbol
3. can't be divided into simpler substances

_____

1. made of two or more elements
2. have a chemical formula
3. can be broken down into simpler substances

_____

1. made of two or more substances
2. do not have a chemical symbol or formula
3. can be separated by physical means

_____

Notes for Home: Your child identified what list items have in common. Give your child a mixture of plastic and metal paper clips and a magnet. Have your child show how to separate the paper clips.

© Pearson Education, Inc.

Name _____

Investigate: How can properties help you separate a mixture?

3–5 Record the part of the mixture that was removed by straining, filtering, and evaporating.

Wear safety goggles.

Separating Method	Results of Separation	
	Part Removed	**Part That Remains**
Straining		
Filtering		
Evaporating		

Explain Your Results

1. Which physical properties did you use to separate the mixture?

_____

_____

_____

© Pearson Education, Inc.

Science Study Notebook

2. Make an **inference** based on the data in your chart. Both sugar and salt dissolve in water. If you used sugar instead of salt, would your results change? Explain.

_____

_____

_____

Go Further

How could you separate a mixture of iron filings, sand, and water? Plan and conduct a simple investigation to answer this question or one of your own.

_____

_____

_____

_____

_____

_____

Notes for Home: Your child did an activity to separate materials in a mixture.
Home Activity: Discuss with your child the techniques you use in the home to separate mixtures. For example, you might separate cooked pasta from water by straining.

© Pearson Education, Inc.

Changes in Matter

In this chapter, you will learn about physical and chemical changes in matter. You will learn that objects are solid, liquid, or gas because of the positions and movement of their atoms or molecules. You will learn that chemical reactions result in chemical changes to matter and that chemical and physical properties can be used to identify materials and separate mixtures.

Tell What You Know

Give examples of three states of matter. How can matter change from one state to another?

_____

Preview the Chapter

Page through each lesson to preview the content and the pictures. Complete the outline by filling in the lesson titles and subheads. Describe your favorite pictures.

Lesson 1: _____

_____

_____

_____

_____

Favorite Picture: _____

Lesson 2: _____

_____

_____

© Pearson Education, Inc.

_____

_____

_____

_____

_____

Favorite Picture: _____

Lesson 3: _____

_____

_____

_____

_____

_____

_____

_____

_____

_____

Favorite Picture: _____

Lesson 4: _____

_____

_____

_____

_____

_____

Favorite Picture: _____

Now you have a Chapter Study Guide. As you read each
lesson, you can write notes on your Study Guide.

Notes for Home: Your child previewed Chapter 2, which tells about the states
of matter and physical and chemical changes in matter. Help your child list
examples of chemical properties and physical properties.

© Pearson Education, Inc.

✂

physical change

Chapter 2, Lesson 1

chemical change

Chapter 2, Lesson 1

evaporation

Chapter 2, Lesson 2

condensation

Chapter 2, Lesson 2

sublimation

Chapter 2, Lesson 2

reactant

Chapter 2, Lesson 3

product

Chapter 2, Lesson 3

chemical equation

Chapter 2, Lesson 3

Directions: Cut out the boxes to use as vocabulary cards.

© Pearson Education, Inc.

a change in which one kind of matter changes into a different kind of matter with different properties

a change in which matter keeps the same chemical properties; a change in size, shape, volume, or state of matter

the process by which particles leave a gas and become a liquid

the process by which particles leave a liquid and become a gas

a substance used in a chemical reaction

the process by which a solid changes directly into a gas

a statement of chemical symbols that shows what happens during a chemical reaction

a substance made by a chemical reaction

Directions: Cut out the boxes to use as vocabulary cards.

© Pearson Education, Inc.

Chapter 2 Vocabulary

Find each word in your glossary at the back of your book.
Read its meaning. Then write the letter of the meaning on the
line next to the word.

_____ **1.** physical change

a. the process by which particles leave a liquid and become a gas

_____ **2.** chemical change

b. a substance used in a chemical reaction

_____ **3.** evaporation

c. a change in which one kind of matter changes into a different kind of matter with different properties

_____ **4.** condensation

d. a substance made by a chemical reaction

_____ **5.** sublimation

e. the process by which a gas becomes a liquid

_____ **6.** reactant

f. a statement of chemical symbols that shows what happens during a chemical reaction

_____ **7.** product

g. the process by which a solid changes directly into a gas

_____ **8.** chemical equation

h. a change in which matter keeps the same chemical properties

Extend Vocabulary

Identify each of these as a physical change or a chemical change.

9. cutting whole carrots into carrot sticks: _____

10. rusting bike: _____

© Pearson Education, Inc.

 Notes for Home: Your child is learning these vocabulary words in Chapter 2. Place a glass of ice on a counter. Have your child check the glass every 5 minutes. Discuss how and why water molecules in the air condensed on the outside of the glass.

Name _____

Use with page 42.

Explore: What can happen during a chemical reaction?

Be careful!

Wear safety goggles.
Do not taste the tablet or liquid.

Record your observations. Color the thermometer.

temperature before reaction	temperature after reaction

Explain Your Results

Think about what you **observed.** Draw a conclusion about how temperature can change during a chemical reaction.

_____

_____

Notes for Home: Your child did an activity about the change of temperature in a chemical reaction.
Home Activity: Discuss with your child why they recorded the temperature of the water before the reaction occurred.

© Pearson Education, Inc.

20 Directed Inquiry

Science Study Notebook

Draw Conclusions

Apply It!

Complete the graphic organizer after reading page 43.

Facts

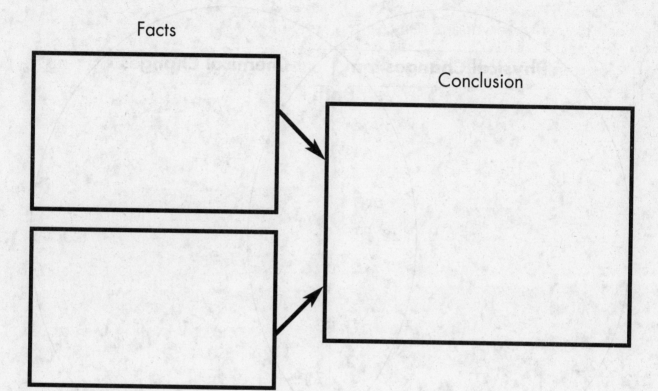

Conclusion

© Pearson Education, Inc.

Name _____

What are physical and chemical changes?

Complete the Venn diagram. Tell how physical changes and chemical changes are alike and different.

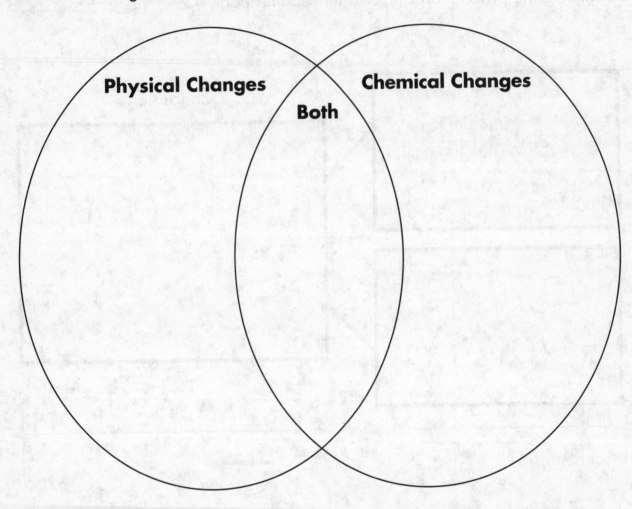

Physical Changes   **Chemical Changes**

Both

Name one example of a physical change and one example of a chemical change.

1. Physical Change _____

_____

2. Chemical Change _____

_____

Notes for Home: Your child compared and contrasted physical changes and chemical changes. Ask your child to show you an example of a physical change.

Science Study Notebook

© Pearson Education, Inc.

How does matter change state?

Identify the properties as those of a solid, liquid, or gas.

1. It has a definite volume but not its own shape. _____

2. Its particles are very far apart. It does not have its own shape or volume. _____

3. It has its own shape and its own volume. _____

Identify the change in state of matter that results from the following physical changes.

Physical Change	State of Matter ——→ State of Matter	
Freezing	——→	
Melting	——→	
Evaporation	——→	
Condensation	——→	
Sublimation	——→	

Notes for Home: Your child identified the changes of state that result from specific physical changes. Ask your child to give examples to illustrate each kind of physical change in the chart.

© Pearson Education, Inc.

What are some kinds of chemical reactions?

1. Label the reactants and the product in the following chemical equation.

$2Mg + O_2$ ⟶ $2MgO$

_____   _____

2. Explain the law of conservation of matter.

_____

_____

_____

3. Name and describe three types of chemical reactions and give an example of each.

Chemical Reactions		
Kind of Reaction	Description	Example

 Notes for Home: Your child identified chemical reactions. Help your child show a combination reaction by allowing steel wool in a soap pad to rust in a cup of water.

© Pearson Education, Inc.

How are chemical properties used?

Summarize the information given for each part of the lesson.

Separating Mixtures
Separating Metals from Ores
Separating Solutions
Identifying Substances

Notes for Home: Your child summarized each section of the lesson to identify ways that chemical properties are used. Ask your child to explain each use.

© Pearson Education, Inc.

Investigate: What is one clue that a chemical reaction has occurred?

3 Use the chart. Record what you **observe** every two minutes for ten minutes.

Wear safety goggles.
Clean up spills right away.

Time (minutes)	Changes Observed
2	
4	
6	
8	
10	

© Pearson Education, Inc.

Explain Your Results

Infer Did a chemical reaction occur? Look at the data you recorded. Explain how your data helps you make your inference.

_____

_____

_____

_____

Go Further

Could temperature affect your results? Plan and conduct an experiment to find out. Write a report explaining your results.

_____

_____

_____

_____

Notes for Home: Your child did an activity about how to identify that a chemical reaction took place.

Home Activity: Ask your child to explain how they knew a new substance was formed.

© Pearson Education, Inc.

Use with pages 76–79.

Experiment: What materials can conduct electricity?

Be careful!

State a hypothesis.

Wear safety goggles.

_____

_____

_____

3 Develop a test to determine if a material conducts electricity. On a separate sheet of paper, identify your variables. Write instructions for your procedure. The instructions should be clear enough that others could follow them.

4 On a separate sheet of paper, explain how your test works.

Collect and record your data.

Record your data on the chart.

Item	Conducts Electricity	Does Not Conduct Electricity
Paper clip		
Short Wire __ cm		
Long Wire __ cm		

Science Study Notebook

© Pearson Education, Inc.

Interpret your data.

Examine the data in your chart.

Which materials conducted electricity? How were they alike?

_____

Which did not conduct electricity? How were they alike?

_____

State your conclusion.

Use your data to make inferences. Then **draw a conclusion** based on your evidence. **Communicate** your conclusion. Does it agree with your hypothesis?

_____

_____

Is further information needed to support your conclusion? Explain.

_____

_____

Go Further

Which conducts heat best, metals or nonmetals? Develop a test to find out. Write a laboratory report. Include your tests, data, evidence, and conclusions. Use a separate sheet of paper, if needed.

_____

_____

_____

_____

_____

Notes for Home: Your child did an activity about conductors of electricity.
Home Activity: Talk with your child about safety rules for using electricity in the home.

© Pearson Education, Inc.

Basic Structures of Organisms

In this chapter, you will learn about the structure of multicellular organisms from their smallest structures, cells, to the organisms themselves. You will also learn how materials are moved through vascular plants and how cells get and use energy.

Tell What You Know

What are the parts of a living thing such as a tree or a dog? What makes up these parts?

_____

Preview the Chapter

Page through each lesson to preview the content and the pictures. Complete the outline by filling in the lesson titles and subheads. Describe your favorite pictures.

Lesson 1: _____

_____

_____

_____

_____

_____

_____

_____

Favorite Picture: _____

© Pearson Education, Inc.

Lesson 2: _____

_____

_____

_____

_____

_____

Favorite Picture: _____

Lesson 3: _____

_____

_____

_____

Favorite Picture: _____

Now you have a Chapter Study Guide. As you read each
lesson, you can write notes on your Study Guide.

Notes for Home: Your child previewed Chapter 3, which tells about the
structural organization of multicellular organisms such as plants and animals.
Help your child list examples of structures in plants.

© Pearson Education, Inc.

✂

vacuole

Chapter 3, Lesson 1

tissue

Chapter 3, Lesson 1

organ

Chapter 3, Lesson 1

vascular

Chapter 3, Lesson 2

xylem

Chapter 3, Lesson 2

phloem

Chapter 3, Lesson 2

chlorophyll

Chapter 3, Lesson 3

chloroplast

Chapter 3, Lesson 3

© Pearson Education, Inc.

 Directions: Cut out the boxes to use as vocabulary cards.

a group of the same kind of cells that work together to do a job

a part of a cell that stores water and nutrients

describes the system of tubes in certain plants that transports water and minerals

a group of different tissues that join together to form one structure

the tubes that carry sugar from a plant's leaves to the rest of the plant

the tubes that carry water and minerals from a plant's roots to its leaves

a structure in plant cells that stores chlorophyll

a green substance that allows plants to make their own food

Directions: Cut out the boxes to use as vocabulary cards.

© Pearson Education, Inc.

Name _____

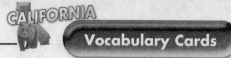
photosynthesis

Chapter 3, Lesson 3

cellular respiration

Chapter 3, Lesson 3

Directions: Cut out the boxes to use as vocabulary cards.

© Pearson Education, Inc.

the process by which cells break down sugar to release energy, water, and carbon dioxide

the process by which plants use carbon dioxide and energy from sunlight to produce oxygen and sugar

Directions: Cut out the boxes to use as vocabulary cards.

© Pearson Education, Inc.

Chapter 3 Vocabulary

Find each word in your glossary at the back of your book.
Read its meaning. Then write the letter of the meaning on the
line next to the word.

____ **1.** vacuole
    a. the tubes that carry water and minerals from a plant's roots to its leaves

____ **2.** tissue
    b. a part of a cell that stores water and nutrients

____ **3.** organ
    c. a structure in plant cells that stores chlorophyll

____ **4.** vascular
    d. describes the system of tubes in certain plants that transport water and minerals

____ **5.** xylem
    e. a group of different tissues that join together to form one structure

____ **6.** phloem
    f. the process by which plants use carbon dioxide, water, and energy from sunlight to make sugar and oxygen

____ **7.** chlorophyll
    g. the tubes that carry sugar from a plant's leaves to the rest of the plant

____ **8.** chloroplast
    h. the process by which cells break down sugar to release energy, water, and carbon dioxide

____ **9.** photosynthesis
    i. a group of the same kind of cells that work together to do a job

____ **10.** cellular respiration
    j. a green substance that allows plants to make their own food

Notes for Home: Your child is learning these vocabulary words in Chapter 3.
Make cards with the words on the front and definitions on the back. Show a
meaning and have your child name the word.

© Pearson Education, Inc.

Explore: What plant structures transport water?

Make a labeled diagram to record your observations (data).

Explain Your Results

1. How did the bottom of the stalk change?

_____

_____

2. Use the labeled diagram to make an **inference** based on your **data.**
What happened to the stalk while it was in the food coloring?

_____

_____

Notes for Home: Your child did an activity about plant structures that transport water.

Home Activity: Discuss with your child what happens to plants when they get the water they need.

© Pearson Education, Inc.

Make Generalizations

Apply It!

Complete the graphic organizer after reading page 93.

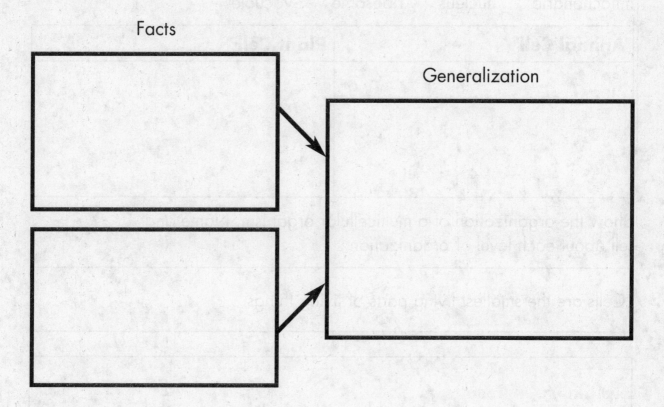

Facts

Generalization

© Pearson Education, Inc.

What makes up multicellular organisms?

Write the name of each cell part in the correct column or columns.

cell membrane   cell wall   chloroplast   cytoplasm
mitochondria   nucleus   ribosome   vacuole

Animal Cell	Plant Cell

Show the organization of a multicellular organism. Name and tell about each level of organization.

Cells are the smallest living parts of living things.

↓

↓

↓

↓

Organism

Notes for Home: Your child identified parts of cells and the structural organization of multicellular organisms. Write each level of organization on its own card. Have your child arrange the cards in order, telling what he or she knows about each level.

© Pearson Education, Inc.

How do materials move through plants?

Use these words to complete the sentences. You may use a word more than once.

bark   fibrous root system   leaves   phloem
roots   stems   taproot   vascular   xylem

1. _____ hold flowers, leaves, and fruit on plants.

2. Higher _____ on plants may get more sunlight needed for food making than lower ones.

3. Plants with a tube system for transporting materials are

   _____ plants.

4. _____ tissue carries water and minerals from the roots to the rest of the plant.

5. _____ tissue carries sugar from the leaves to the other parts of the plant.

6. In trees _____, which is made up of dead phloem, protects the phloem beneath it.

7. When celery is placed in a cup of red dye and water, the parts of

   celery that turn red show where the _____ is.

8. A _____ is a large root that grows straight down and may have smaller roots growing sideways out of it.

9. _____ are the organ of the plant that anchor it to the ground and hold it in place.

10. In a _____, roots grow out in all directions.

Notes for Home: Your child completed sentences about plants. With your child, put a celery stalk in a glass of water and red dye and leave it overnight. Have your child explain what happened to the stalk.

© Pearson Education, Inc.

How do cells get and use energy?

Write *photosynthesis* or *cellular respiration* to tell what the equation stands for. Then answer the questions that follow.

sugar + oxygen ⟶ carbon dioxide + water + energy

_____

$$\text{carbon dioxide + water} \xrightarrow[\text{chlorophyll}]{\text{light energy}} \text{sugar + oxygen}$$

_____

1. What are two reasons why animals rely on photosynthesis in plants for survival?

_____

_____

_____

_____

2. How are photosynthesis and cellular respiration reverse operations?

_____

_____

_____

_____

3. What do the processes of photosynthesis and cellular respiration form?

_____

_____

Notes for Home: Your child identified equations for photosynthesis and cellular respiration and answered questions about the processes. Ask your child to explain the carbon dioxide-oxygen cycle.

Science Study Notebook

© Pearson Education, Inc.

Name _____

Investigate: How do plants use carbon dioxide?

Wear safety goggles.
Do not drink water with BTB in it.
Use the straw to breathe out only!
Do not breathe in.

3–**4** Use the chart. Record what you observe.

	Color of Water with BTB	**Time** (quantitative observation)
Before breathing out into the water		
After breathing out into the water		
Immediately after adding elodea to the water		0 minutes
When the water turns blue		_____ minutes

© Pearson Education, Inc.

Science Study Notebook

Explain Your Results

1. What made the color change when you breathed into the water?

_____

_____

2. What made the color change when you added elodea?

_____

_____

What quantitative **observation** did you record?

_____

_____

Go Further

Elodea is an aquatic plant. Use library resources to **classify** 20 plants based on their habitat needs.

_____

_____

_____

_____

_____

_____

_____

_____

Notes for Home: Your child did an activity about how plants use carbon dioxide.
Home Activity: Talk with your child about the importance of plants in producing the oxygen animals need to breathe.

© Pearson Education, Inc.

Human Body Systems

In this chapter, you will learn about the circulatory, respiratory, digestive, and urinary systems in the human body. You will learn about the structures in each system and their functions.

Tell What You Know

How does your body get the food and air it needs?

_____

Preview the Chapter

Page through each lesson to preview the content and the pictures. Complete the outline by filling in the lesson titles and subheads. Describe your favorite pictures.

Lesson 1: _____

_____

_____

_____

Favorite Picture: _____

Lesson 2: _____

_____

_____

Favorite Picture: _____

© Pearson Education, Inc.

Lesson 3: _____

_____

_____

_____

_____

_____

Favorite Picture: _____

Now you have a Chapter Study Guide. As you read each
lesson, you can write notes on your Study Guide.

Notes for Home: Your child previewed Chapter 4, which tells about systems
of the human body and their structures and functions. Help your child name
systems of the body and their structures.

© Pearson Education, Inc.

artery

Chapter 4, Lesson 1

capillary

Chapter 4, Lesson 1

vein

Chapter 4, Lesson 1

trachea

Chapter 4, Lesson 2

bronchiole

Chapter 4, Lesson 2

air sacs

Chapter 4, Lesson 2

digestion

Chapter 4, Lesson 3

esophagus

Chapter 4, Lesson 3

Directions: Cut out the boxes to use as vocabulary cards.

© Pearson Education, Inc.

✂

the smallest kind of blood vessels	a blood vessel that carries blood away from the heart to other parts of the body
the tube that carries air from the larynx to the lungs	a blood vessel that carries blood toward the heart
the thin-walled sacs in the lungs where oxygen enters the blood and carbon dioxide leaves the blood	a small tube in the lungs that carries air to air sacs
the tube that carries food from the mouth to the stomach	the process that changes food into a form that the body can use

© Pearson Education, Inc.

 Directions: Cut out the boxes to use as vocabulary cards.

winding tube where
nged chemically and
vn into small particles
absorbed into the

Chapter 4, Lesson 3

collects and stores
ed by the kidneys

Chapter 4, Lesson 3

ntestine

and carbon di

blood

© Pearson Education, Inc.

rds.

Name _____

a wider tube connected to the small intestine that removes water from undigested food and stores this waste until it is removed from the body

a narrow,
food is ch
broken do
that can b
blood

the sac th
urine form

Directions: Cut out the boxes to use as vocabulary

Name _____

Chapter 4 Vocabulary

Find each word in your glossary at the back of your book.
Read its meaning. Then write the letter of the meaning on the
line next to the word.

____ **1.** artery

____ **2.** capillary

____ **3.** vein

____ **4.** trachea

____ **5.** bronchiole

____ **6.** air sacs

____ **7.** digestion

____ **8.** esophagus

____ **9.** small intestine

____ **10.** large intestine

____ **11.** bladder

a. a blood vessel that carries blood toward the heart

b. a wider tube connected to the small intestine that removes water from undigested food and stores this waste until it is removed from the body

c. a small tube in the lungs that carries air to air sacs

d. the process that changes food into a form that the body can use

e. a narrow, winding tube where food is changed chemically and broken down into small particles that can be absorbed into the blood

f. the thin-walled sacs in the lungs where oxygen enters the blood and carbon dioxide leaves the blood

g. a blood vessel that carries blood away from the heart to other parts of the body

h. the tube that carries air from the larynx to the lungs

i. the tube that carries food from the mouth to the stomach

j. the sac that collects and stores urine formed by the kidneys

k. the smallest kind of blood vessels

Notes for Home: Notes for Home: Your child is learning these vocabulary words in Chapter 4. Name a structure and have your child tell what the structure does.

© Pearson Education, Inc.

Explore: How can you observe your pulse?

Explain Your Results

1. Describe the movements of the straw you **observed** in your **investigation.**

_____

_____

2. What caused the straw to move?

_____

_____

_____

Notes for Home: Your child did an activity about observing the pulse.
Home Activity: Discuss with your child how the doctor takes your pulse.

© Pearson Education, Inc.

Sequence

Apply It!

Complete the graphic organizer after reading page 125.

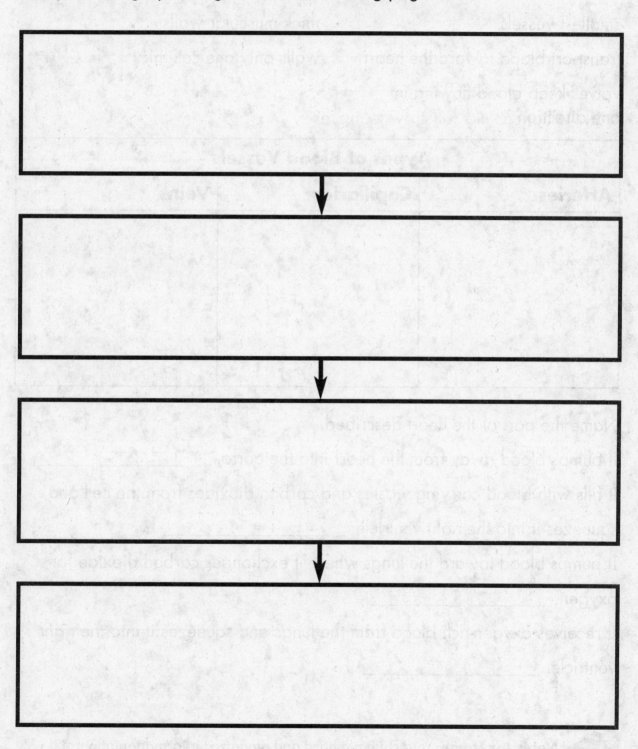

© Pearson Education, Inc.

How does blood circulate?

Complete the chart. Write each characteristic where it fits in the chart.

carry blood away from the heart   gases pass through the thin walls

smallest vessels   thick muscular walls

transport blood toward the heart   walls only one cell thick

valves keep blood flowing in
one direction

Types of Blood Vessels		
Arteries	**Capillaries**	**Veins**

Name the part of the heart described.

It pumps blood away from the heart into the aorta. _____

It fills with blood carrying wastes and carbon dioxides from the cell and

squeezes it into the right ventricle. _____

It pumps blood toward the lungs where it exchanges carbon dioxide for

oxygen. _____

It receives oxygen-rich blood from the lungs and squeezes it into the right

ventricle. _____

Notes for Home: Your child provided and organized information about the
circulatory system. Have your child tell you how the heart works.

© Pearson Education, Inc.

What is the respiratory system?

Tell about each of these structures of the respiratory system.
Then answer the question.

Sinuses: _____

_____

Larynx: _____

_____

Trachea: _____

_____

Bronchi: _____

_____

Bronchioles: _____

_____

Air sacs: _____

_____

Summarize how the respiratory system and the circulatory
system work together.

_____

_____

_____

_____

_____

 Notes for Home: Your child identified parts of the respiratory system and told
how the respiratory system and circulatory system work together. Have your child
draw a picture to show and tell you about how the lungs work.

© Pearson Education, Inc.

What are the digestive and urinary systems?

Write the name of each organ in the chart where it belongs.
Tell what each organ does.

bladder   esophagus   kidneys
salivary glands   small intestine   stomach

Digestive System	Urinary System

 Notes for Home: Your child completed a chart to show parts of the digestive and urinary systems. Ask your child to tell you about the digestive process.

© Pearson Education, Inc.

Investigate: What is your lung capacity?

Be careful!

④ Make a bar graph of the lung capacities of all the students in your class.

Do not inhale through the straw! Wear safety goggles.

Number of Students

15
14
13
12
11
10
9
8
7
6
5
4
3
2
1
0   0–1   1–2   2–3   3–4

Lung Capacity (liters)

© Pearson Education, Inc.

Name _____

CALIFORNIA
Lab zone **Guided Inquiry**
Use with pages 144–145.

Explain Your Results

1. Make an **inference** using the data in your bar graph.
State your conclusion.

_____

_____

2. Examine your conclusion. Do you have enough information to make this conclusion? What else would you need to know? How would you gather this information?

_____

_____

_____

_____

Go Further

Does posture affect how much air you can breathe in and out? Make and carry out a plan to investigate this or another question.

© Pearson Education, Inc.

Notes for Home: Your child did an activity about lung capacity.
Home Activity: Have your child explain the activity. Talk about whether you would expect to have greater lung capacity or less capacity than your child.

Name _____

Experiment: How does exercise affect heart rate?

State a hypothesis.

_____

_____

Be careful!

Let your teacher know if you have trouble exercising because of a health condition.

Identify and control variables.

What is the independent variable? What is the dependent variable? What is one controlled variable?

_____

_____

How does identifying a single independent variable help you collect information to answer questions about the results of your experiment?

_____

_____

Collect and record your data.

Record your data on the chart. *Pulse = 2 X Number of Beats in 30 Seconds*

| Student | Before Exercise | | After Exercise | | Student | Before Exercise | | After Exercise | |
	Number of Beats in 30 Seconds	*Pulse (beats per minute)	Number of Beats in 30 Seconds	*Pulse (beats per minute)		Number of Beats in 30 Seconds	*Pulse (beats per minute)	Number of Beats in 30 Seconds	*Pulse (beats per minute)
1					16				
2					27				
3					18				
4					19				
5					20				
6					21				
7					22				
8					23				
9					24				
10					25				
11					26				
12					27				
13					28				
14					29				
15					30				

© Pearson Education, Inc.

Interpret your data.

Make and use graphs to help you interpret and **make inferences** based on your data.

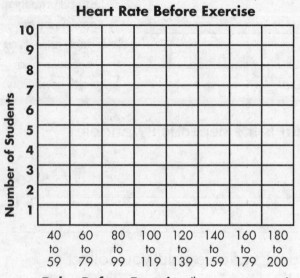

Heart Rate Before Exercise

Pulse Before Exercise (beats per minute)

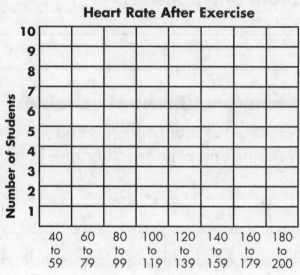

Heart Rate After Exercise

Pulse After Exercise (beats per minute)

State your conclusion.

Compare your results and hypothesis.

_____

Make an **inference** based on your data. How does exercise affect your heart rate? **Communicate** your conclusion.

_____

Go Further

Predict How might exercising for more than one minute affect your heart rate? Use this question or develop another testable question. Plan and conduct a simple investigation. Write instructions that others could follow.

Notes for Home: Your child did an activity about the effects of exercise on heart rate.
Home Activity: Discuss with your child how he or she measured heart rate by taking a pulse.

© Pearson Education, Inc.

Water on Earth

In this chapter, you will learn about water on the Earth—salt water in the oceans and fresh water in rivers, lakes, and glaciers. You will learn about the water cycle and the different kinds of clouds and precipitations. You will also learn about water processing and the sources of water in California.

Tell What You Know

What bodies of fresh water or ocean are near where you live? How do people use this water?

_____

Preview the Chapter

Page through each lesson to preview the content and the pictures. Complete the outline by filling in the lesson titles and subheads. Describe your favorite pictures.

Lesson 1: _____

_____

_____

_____

_____

Favorite Picture: _____

Lesson 2: _____

_____

_____

_____

_____

_____

_____

_____

© Pearson Education, Inc.

Favorite Picture: _____

Lesson 3: _____

_____

_____

_____

_____

_____

Favorite Picture: _____

Lesson 4: _____

_____

_____

_____

_____

Favorite Picture: _____

Lesson 5: _____

_____

_____

_____

_____

_____

Favorite Picture: _____

Now you have a Chapter Study Guide. As you read each
lesson, you can write notes on your Study Guide.

Notes for Home: Your child previewed Chapter 5, which tells about Earth's
water. Discuss with your child the sources of water used in your home.

© Pearson Education, Inc.

✂

sea level	**salinity**
Chapter 5, Lesson 1	Chapter 5, Lesson 1
aquifer	**water table**
Chapter 5, Lesson 2	Chapter 5, Lesson 2
watershed	**reservoir**
Chapter 5, Lesson 2	Chapter 5, Lesson 2
water cycle	**evaporation**
Chapter 5, Lesson 4	Chapter 5, Lesson 4

Directions: Cut out the boxes to use as vocabulary cards.

© Pearson Education, Inc.

a measure of the amount of salt in water

the level of the surface of an ocean

the top level of the groundwater in an aquifer

the layer of rock and soil that groundwater flows through

usually an artificial lake that forms behind a dam

the area from which water drains into a river

the process by which particles leave a liquid and become a gas

the repeated movement of water through the environment in different forms; also called the hydrologic cycle

 Directions: Cut out the boxes to use as vocabulary cards.

© Pearson Education, Inc.

condensation

Chapter 5, Lesson 4

precipitation

Chapter 5, Lesson 4

sleet

Chapter 5, Lesson 5

© Pearson Education, Inc.

Directions: Cut out the boxes to use as vocabulary cards.

the water that falls from clouds as rain, hail, sleet, or snow

the process by which particles leave a gas and become a liquid

the frozen raindrops that fall as precipitation

Directions: Cut out the boxes to use as vocabulary cards.

© Pearson Education, Inc.

Chapter 5 Vocabulary

Find each word in your glossary at the back of your book.
Read its meaning. Then write the letter of the meaning on the
line next to the word.

____ **1.** sea level

a. the area from which water drains into a river

____ **2.** salinity

b. the level of the surface of an ocean

____ **3.** aquifer

c. usually an artificial lake that forms behind a dam

____ **4.** water table

d. the process by which a gas becomes a liquid

____ **5.** watershed

e. the frozen raindrops that fall as precipitation

____ **6.** reservoir

f. a measure of the amount of salt in water

____ **7.** water cycle

g. the water that falls from clouds as rain, hail, sleet, or snow

____ **8.** condensation

h. the repeated movement of water through the environment in different forms; also called the hydrologic cycle

____ **9.** evaporation

i. the layer of rock and soil that groundwater flows through

____ **10.** precipitation

j. the top level of the groundwater in an aquifer

____ **11.** sleet

k. the process by which particles leave a liquid and become a gas

Notes for Home: Your child is learning these vocabulary words in Chapter 5. Have your child write each word on one side of a card and use words or pictures to define it on the other side. Then he or she can use the cards as a study tool.

© Pearson Education, Inc.

Explore: Where is Earth's water?

Explain Your Results

Infer Based on your model draw a conclusion about the need to conserve fresh water. Explain.

_____

_____

_____

_____

Notes for Home: Your child did an activity about how much of Earth's water is fresh water.
Home Activity: Talk with your child about what you and your family can do to help conserve water.

© Pearson Education, Inc.

Name _____

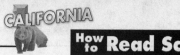

Main Idea and Details

Apply It!

Complete the graphic organizer after reading page 171.

Main Idea

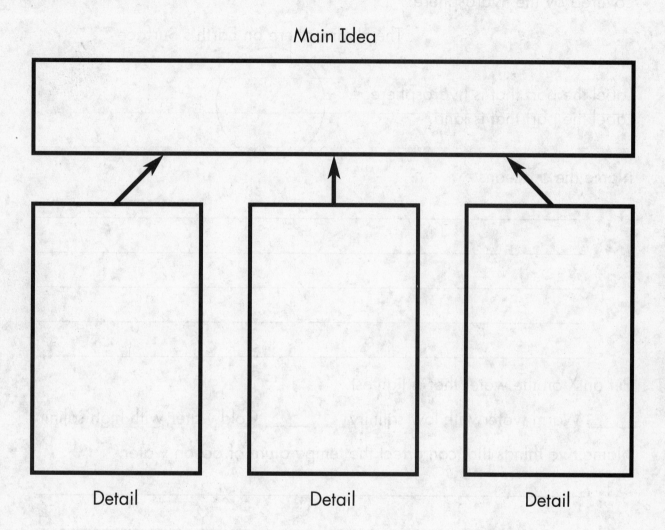

Detail   Detail   Detail

© Pearson Education, Inc.

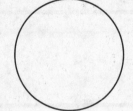

How can the oceans be described?

Read the lesson. Then follow the directions.

Draw a circle graph. Show the amount of Earth's surface covered by the hydrosphere.

The Hydrosphere on Earth's Surface

Label the part that is hydrosphere.
Label the part that is land.

Name the 5 oceans.

1. _____

2. _____

3. _____

4. _____

5. _____

Put an X on the water that is lightest.

_____ Warm water with low salinity   _____ Cold water with high salinity

Name two things that can affect the temperature of ocean water.

1. _____

2. _____

Name three resources that come from ocean water.

1. _____

2. _____

3. _____

 Notes for Home: Your child answered questions about the oceans. Talk with your child about any experiences you or your child may have had with the oceans.

© Pearson Education, Inc.

Where is fresh water found?

Read the lesson. Add the terms and phrases where they belong in the chart.

aquifer	creek
glaciers	icebergs
ice sheets	reservoir
$\frac{7}{10}$ of Earth's fresh water	surrounded by higher land
underground water	water collects in low spot
watershed	water table

Fresh Water on Earth			
Groundwater	Ice	Lakes	Rivers

Notes for Home: Your child organized information about fresh water sources in a chart. Have your child tell you the difference between a natural lake and a reservoir.

© Pearson Education, Inc.

What are some California water sources?

Read the lesson. Then use the terms in the box to complete the sentences.

California Aqueduct	Colorado River Aqueduct	Lake Tahoe
Los Angeles Aqueduct	northern coastal region	reclamation
southeastern California	watershed	

1. The _____ of California gets about 250 centimeters of rain in a year.

2. The deserts of _____ get only about 10 centimeters of rain per year.

3. The _____ carries water from the mouth of the Sacramento River hundreds of kilometers south.

4. Part of the _____ is nearly 100 years old and was built to carry water from east side of the Sierra Nevada.

5. The _____ provides the city of San Diego with much of its water.

6. In _____, wastewater is sent to a treatment plant to be treated for reuse.

7. _____ is on the northeastern border with Nevada.

8. Harmful chemicals used on land in a _____ can be carried by runoff into rivers and streams.

Notes for Home: Your child completed sentences about California water. Talk with your child about sources of water in your community.

© Pearson Education, Inc.

What is the water cycle?

Look at the diagram of the water cycle. Label the cycle with these terms.

condensation   evaporation   precipitation

Answer these questions.

1. What is runoff?

_____

2. What does condensation form?

_____

3. Why does evaporation make ocean water saltier?

_____

_____

Notes for Home: Your child labeled a diagram and answered questions about the water cycle. Ask your child to explain the water cycle to you. Encourage him or her to use visuals.

© Pearson Education, Inc.

Name _____

How do clouds form?

Name each kind of cloud.

1. ground-level cloud:

_____

2. vertical clouds that can cause thunderstorms:

_____

3. low-altitude clouds that cover whole sky:

_____

4. high-altitude clouds that are thin, wispy, and white:

_____

5. mid-altitude clouds that look like small, puffy balls:

_____

Tell how sleet and hailstones are formed differently.

_____

_____

_____

_____

_____

_____

_____

© Pearson Education, Inc.

Notes for Home: Your child identified clouds and explained how sleet and hailstones are formed differently. Ask your child to identify clouds you can see today.

Name _____

Investigate: What is a cloud?

4—**5** Record your observations in the chart.

Wipe up spills right away.

Time	Observations	
	Bowl with Warm Water	**Bowl Without Water**
After 1 minute		
After 5 minutes		
After 10 minutes		

Name _____

Explain Your Results

1. Make an **inference** based on your **models.** Is water vapor in the air when clouds form? Explain.

_____

_____

2. Use your results to describe conditions necessary for clouds to form.

_____

_____

Go Further

Does temperature have an effect on the results? Design and conduct a scientific investigation to answer this question or one of your own. Describe and demonstrate how to perform your investigation safely.

_____

_____

_____

_____

_____

_____

_____

_____

 Notes for Home: Your child did an activity about the formation of clouds.
Home Activity: Have your child explain the activity. Ask if you would expect to see more clouds when the air is humid or when it is dry.

Weather

In this chapter, you will learn about weather and how it changes. You will learn about moving air masses and about severe forms of weather such as tornadoes and hurricanes. You will also learn about the tools used to measure weather and about weather forecasting.

Tell What You Know

What do you consider good weather? Bad weather?

_____

Preview the Chapter

Page through each lesson to preview the content and the pictures. Complete the outline by filling in the lesson titles and subheads. Describe your favorite pictures.

Lesson 1: _____

_____

_____

_____

_____

Favorite Picture: _____

Lesson 2: _____

_____

_____

_____

_____

_____

Favorite Picture: _____

Lesson 3: _____

_____

_____

_____

_____

Favorite Picture: _____

Lesson 4: _____

_____

_____

_____

_____

_____

_____

Favorite Picture: _____

Now you have a Chapter Study Guide. As you read each
lesson, you can write notes on your Study Guide.

Notes for Home: Your child previewed Chapter 6, which tells about weather and
weather forecasting. Discuss with your child reasons why people are interested in
daily weather forecasts.

atmospheric pressure Chapter 6, Lesson 1	**convection current** Chapter 6, Lesson 1
wind Chapter 6, Lesson 1	**air mass** Chapter 6, Lesson 2
front Chapter 6, Lesson 2	**cyclone** Chapter 6, Lesson 2
tempered Chapter 6, Lesson 3	**barometer** Chapter 6, Lesson 4

 Directions: Cut out the boxes to use as vocabulary cards.

the rising and sinking of matter in a circular pattern caused by temperature differences

the weight of air pushing down on an area

a large body of air with similar properties all through it

the convection currents in the atmosphere

a wind that spirals inward around an area of low pressure

a boundary between two air masses

a tool that measures air pressure

describes air that is warmed in winter and cooled in summer because it is near a large body of water

Directions: Cut out the boxes to use as vocabulary cards.

✂

anemometer

Chapter 6, Lesson 4

rain gauge

Chapter 6, Lesson 4

Directions: Cut out the boxes to use as vocabulary cards.

a tool that measures the amount of rain that has fallen

a tool that measures wind speed

 Directions: Cut out the boxes to use as vocabulary cards.

Name _____

CALIFORNIA
Lab zone **Guided Inquiry**
Use with pages 242–243.

2. Relate your **observations** to warm and cold convection currents found in the air.

_____

_____

_____

_____

_____

_____

Go Further

Investigate further to find a way to make two convection systems in the tub.

© Pearson Education, Inc.

Notes for Home: Your child did an activity about convection currents.
Home Activity: Ask your child to draw a diagram to help you understand the flow of convection currents as he or she explains the activity.

all the objects
anets and the
, comets, and
the force that

nets that orbit it?

and the
son titles

© Pearson Education, Inc.

lls about the solar
ved us noodles to help
Venus, Earth, Mars,

ience Study Notebook

Name _____

Lesson 3: _____

Favorite Picture: _____

Lesson 4: _____

Favorite Picture: _____

Now you have a Chapter Study Guide. As you read eac
lesson, you can write notes on your Study Guide.

Notes for Home: Your child previewed Chapter 7, which t
system. Introduce the mnemonic *My very eager mother just s*
them remember the names of the known planets—Mercury
Jupiter, Saturn, Uranus, Neptune.

✂

star	**solar system**
Chapter 7, Lesson 1	Chapter 7, Lesson 1
ellipse	**planet**
Chapter 7, Lesson 2	Chapter 7, Lesson 2
satellite	**asteroid**
Chapter 7, Lesson 2	Chapter 7, Lesson 3
comet	
Chapter 7, Lesson 3	

Directions: Cut out the boxes to use as vocabulary cards.

© Pearson Education, Inc.

a system that includes the Sun and its planets, along with many moons, asteroids, and comets

a huge ball of very hot gas that gives off energy

a large, round object that moves around a star, such as the Sun

a shape like an oval

a rocky object up to several hundred kilometers wide that revolves around the Sun

an object that orbits another object in space

a frozen mass of ice and dust with a tail up to 80 million kilometers long that is in orbit around the Sun

Directions: Cut out the boxes to use as vocabulary cards.

© Pearson Education, Inc.

Chapter 7 Vocabulary

Find each word in your glossary at the back of your book.
Read its meaning. Then write the letter of the meaning on the
line next to the word.

____ **1.** star

a. a large, round object that moves around a star, such as the Sun

____ **2.** solar system

b. a huge ball of very hot gas that gives off energy

____ **3.** ellipse

c. a frozen mass of ice and dust with a tail up to 80 million kilometers long that is in orbit around the Sun

____ **4.** planet

d. a rocky object up to several hundred kilometers wide that revolves around the Sun

____ **5.** satellite

e. an object that orbits another object in space

____ **6.** asteroid

f. a shape like an oval

____ **7.** comet

g. a system that includes the Sun and its planets, along with many moons, asteroids, and comets

Name three different kinds of solar satellites.

_____

Tell what is at the center of the solar system.

_____

Notes for Home: Your child is learning these vocabulary words in Chapter 7.
Encourage your child to use each word in a sentence that supports its meaning.

© Pearson Education, Inc.

Explore: What is the shape of a planet's path?

Be careful!

Wear safety goggles.

2 **Observe** the shape. Is the length from the center to the edge the same in all directions?

_____

Explain Your Results

Infer How would moving the second pin farther from the center affect the shape of the new ellipse?

_____

_____

Notes for Home: Your child did an activity about the shape of a planet's orbit.
Home Activity: Talk with your child about how distances from the center to the edge are the same in a circle but different in an ellipse.

© Pearson Education, Inc.

Make Inferences

Apply It!

Complete the graphic organizer after reading page 255.

Facts

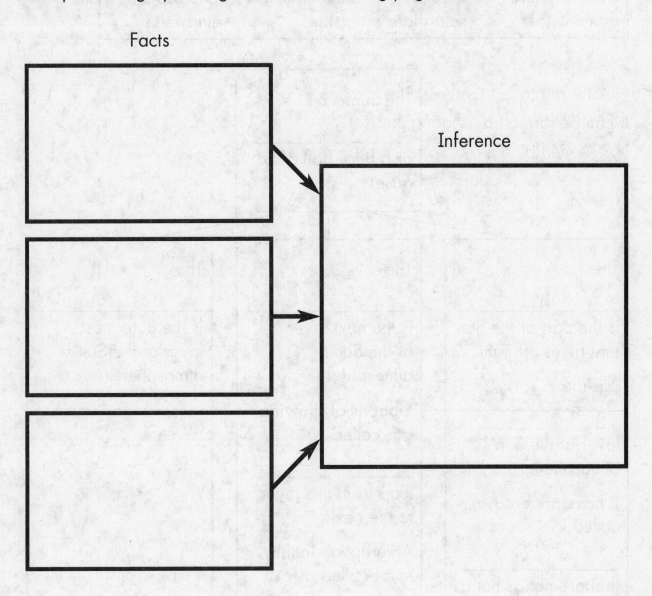

Inference

© Pearson Education, Inc.

What is the Sun?

Read the lesson. Use the words in the box to complete the concept web.

chromosphere	corona	innermost	photosphere
prominences	solar flare	star	sunspots

The Sun is a

_____,

or a fiery ball of hot gases.

The

_____

is the part of the Sun that gives off light.

It is the

_____

layer of the Sun's atmosphere.

It has dark areas called

_____

that are not as hot as the rest of the layer.

The

_____

is the next layer of the Sun's atmosphere.

Ribbons of glowing gas called

_____

leap from this layer to the next.

An eruption in this layer called a

_____

causes a temporary bright spot.

The

_____

is the outermost layer of the Sun's atmosphere.

 Notes for Home: Your child completed a concept web identifying information about the Sun. Ask your child to draw a model of the Sun showing the layers of its atmosphere.

© Pearson Education, Inc.

Why do planets revolve around the Sun?

Read the lesson. Use the words in the box to complete the sentences.

ellipses	gravity	inner planets	mass	Mercury
Moon	orbit	outer planets	satellite	

1. The Sun and its planets are attracted to each other by

_____.

2. The Sun has much more _____ than any other object
in the solar system.

3. Gravity causes the planets to move in _____ around
the Sun.

4. The four planets closest to the Sun are the _____.

5. The four planets farthest from the Sun are the _____.

6. A _____ is an object that orbits another object in
space.

7. Because it orbits Earth, the _____ is a satellite of
Earth.

8. All of the planets except Venus and _____ have at
least one satellite orbiting them.

9. Gravity between the satellites and their planets keep the satellites in
_____ around the planets.

Notes for Home: Your child completed sentences about gravity in the solar
system. Ask your child to explain why the Moon remains in orbit around Earth.

© Pearson Education, Inc.

What are the inner planets?

Read the lesson. Then write each characteristic in the chart
where it fits. You may use one of the characteristics two times.

asteroid belt between it and Jupiter

covered with red soil made of iron oxide

88 Earth days in a year

second planet from the Sun

225 Earth Days in a year

atmosphere with gases used by living things

covered with craters made by meteorites

very hot in daytime, very cold at night

covered by thick, swirling clouds

planet closest to the Sun

686 Earth days in a year

365 Earth days in a year

almost no atmosphere

has liquid water

2 moons

poisonous atmosphere

extremely hot

third planet from the Sun

fourth planet from the Sun

1 Moon

largest rocky planet

no moon

Mercury	Venus	Earth	Mars

Notes for Home: Notes for Home: Your child identified characteristics of the
inner planets. Ask your child to draw the inner planets with their moons in orbit
around the Sun.

© Pearson Education, Inc.

What do we know about the outer planets and beyond?

Read the lesson. Then write each characteristic in the chart where it fits. You may use some characteristics more than once.

a year that is 165 Earth years long   a gas giant

a year that is 29.4 Earth years long   smallest gas giant

a year that is 12 Earth years long   at least 34 moons

rotates on its side   at least 13 moons

at least 63 moons   has rings

largest planet   at least 27 moons

a year that is 84 Earth years long

Jupiter	Saturn	Uranus	Neptune

 Notes for Home: Your child identified characteristics of the outer planets. Ask your child to add these planets to their drawing of the inner planets around the Sun.

© Pearson Education, Inc.

Investigate: How do space probes send images of the solar system?

3–4 Work with a partner who has an Image Sending Grid. Ask about each grid space. Fill that space in on the Image Receiving Grid if your partner says "1." Do not fill it in if your partner says "0."

Image Receiving Grid

	A	B	C	D	E	F	G	H	I	J
1										
2										
3										
4										
5										
6										
7										
8										
9										
10										

5 Compare the images. Are they the same? Explain.

_____

_____

© Pearson Education, Inc.

Explain Your Results

1. How accurately was the signal received? Explain why the new image might not be perfectly accurate.

_____

_____

_____

2. Based on the process you **modeled,** describe how the image is sent from a space probe.

_____

_____

_____

_____

_____

3. **Infer** How do you think cameras on satellites orbiting Earth send images back to Earth?

_____

Go Further

What would happen if you "sent" a partner a full-page picture drawn on a piece of graph paper with large squares and one drawn on a piece with small squares? Find out. Send both to a partner with matching graph paper. Does one take longer? Does one make a better picture?

_____

_____

_____

_____

Notes for Home: Your child did an activity about sending and receiving images from space probes.
Home Activity: Have your child show you the grids and explain the activity to you.

© Pearson Education, Inc.

Name _____

Experiment: What is one cause for the uneven heating of Earth?

The bulb will get hot.
Do not touch it.

State a hypothesis.

_____

_____

_____

Identify and control variables.

In this experiment, what is the independent variable? What is the dependent variable? What is the controlled variable?

_____

_____

Collect and record your data.

Angle measure	Starting Temperature (°C)	Temperature After 3 Minutes (°C)
30° angle	°C	°C
60° angle	°C	°C
90° angle	°C	°C

Interpret your data.

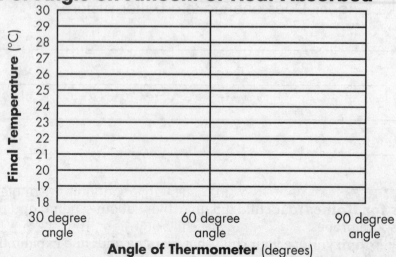

Effect of Angle on Amount of Heat Absorbed

© Pearson Education, Inc.

Science Study Notebook

Examine how the final temperature (the dependent variable) varies with the angle of the thermometer.

_____

_____

State your conclusion.

How did the final temperature vary with the angle of the thermometer?

_____

_____

Compare your hypothesis and results.

_____

_____

Communicate your conclusion. Do you need further information to support your conclusion? Explain.

_____

_____

You collect information about the independent variable. Explain how this helped you answer the main question in the experiment.

_____

_____

Go Further

Does the Sun heat land and water the same? Plan and conduct a simple investigation to answer this question or develop a testable question of your own. Write clear instructions others could follow.

Notes for Home: Your child did an activity about how the angle of light affects the amount of heat an object gets.
Home Activity: Discuss with your child how light from the Sun heats Earth's poles less than Earth's equator.

© Pearson Education, Inc.